Dear Amy,

Thank you so much for your support! May you have a blessed 2020!

Sincerely,

Taran Lancaster

The Fragments of a Child Life Intern

Taran Lancaster

For the children, families, and staff who
have contributed to my growth as a
child life specialist.

Table of Contents

Preface

When I was in elementary school, a dear friend of mine was diagnosed with cancer. From that moment forward, I was determined to spend my life working with hospitalized children and their families. However, I struggled with finding a healthcare role that appealed to me. I had no interest in research, nor did I possess any skills in mathematics. What I *did* have was a strong skill set in compassion, empathy, and psychology.

I first discovered the field of child life while visiting my brother's college, which is now my alma mater. Child life specialists rely on their intensive knowledge of development to help a child and their family understand and cope with illness, trauma, and loss. This is achieved by utilizing developmentally appropriate interventions, such as preparation for medical events, distraction during procedures, sibling support, therapeutic play, medical-based play, and diagnostic teachings. Ideally, child life specialists put a sometimes scary environment in a language that children and their families can understand and be comfortable with. Child life specialists can be found in children's hospitals, dental offices, advocacy centers, funeral homes, schools, and in your community.

In order to become a child life specialist, one must complete a verified child life internship. These internships are extremely competitive and are offered three times a year to select students across the country. Despite the competition, I declared a major in child life and spent four years of my college career diversifying my résumé. When I wasn't in class, I could be found volunteering at multiple children's hospitals, co-facilitating sessions at a grief center, mentoring young adults with cognitive and physical disabilities, assisting at an elementary school, and everywhere else in between.

After applying for twelve child life internships during my senior year, I interviewed with seven incredible programs across the country. During the national offer week, I received five child life internship offers and gratefully accepted one.

When my child life internship began, I was beaming in my knowledge of child development and medical terminology. Thanks to my schooling, I had resources for every theory and practice necessary. However, I learned very quickly that there was one resource I was greatly missing. I didn't have a book to turn to when I struggled with switching rotations or when I felt out of place. I had an excellent support system, but I didn't have anything tangible to hold while I shoveled ice cream into my mouth at ten in the morning after experiencing my first death of a child.

I had dozens of books on conditions and theorists, so why didn't I have a book on the lost and disoriented twenty-two-year-old child life intern? Unfortunately, I couldn't find the type of resource I yearned for, so I created one. When I returned home from my child life internship each day, I wrote a fragment. One fragment turned into a collection of fragments, and then some more. What began merely as a coping mechanism turned into a story that demanded to be told.

Of course, some details have been altered and/

or omitted due to each child's and family's rights to protection of their privacy. It was always my intention to write about my experience first. I wanted to focus on the story that I have the right to tell, which is my own. I want you to know that I claim to be no master of poetry. I am no master of writing. I simply wanted to convey my emotions and experiences in each line of text. If you're looking for something with prose perfection, continue browsing, please.

Finally, thank you for reading and thank you for giving back. I will be donating 10 percent of proceeds from paperbacks sold to a local child life program, along with an additional 10 percent of proceeds from paperbacks sold to the Agrace Grief Support Center. I hope you enjoy a glimpse into the life of a child life intern.

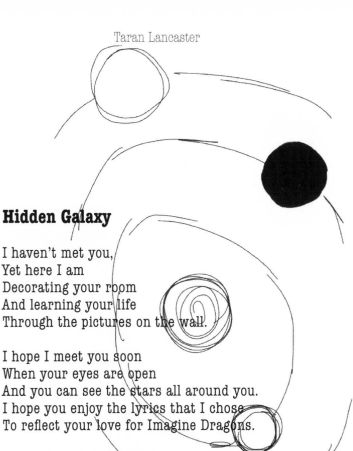

Hidden Galaxy

I haven't met you,
Yet here I am
Decorating your room
And learning your life
Through the pictures on the wall.

I hope I meet you soon
When your eyes are open
And you can see the stars all around you.
I hope you enjoy the lyrics that I chose
To reflect your love for Imagine Dragons.

If I never get to meet you
In this life or the next,
Please know that space is an infinity,
Your spirit can outshine the sun,
And we are all lost stars flickering as one.

I'll Read to You Tomorrow

I wish that I could go back
To another Wednesday afternoon,
When you were making fun of me
Because I didn't know how to play the game,
And you were letting me into your world.

But this Wednesday is different.
You're intubated in the PICU,
And my heart is tied in knots,
As your aunt recognizes who I am
And her arms welcome me home.

And then I turn to you.
I squeeze your hand three times
And tell you how much I miss you,
Because I know you can hear me,
Because I can hear your heart beating.

We say what we hope is true,
That this won't be the last time,
But that is out of my control,
And your contagious laugh leaves me saying,
"I don't want to let go . . ."

Graduation Parties

It absolutely floors me that
You had a brain shunt
Placed only yesterday,
Yet here we are discussing the career of Pete Wentz
And questioning the absence of Ellen Degeneres.

What I learned today will stay with me always.
The communication between ventricles in the brain
Is a miraculous and complex concept
That I will never understand.

But what I do know
Is that you deserve the utmost respect.
And when meeting your family,
I am so confident
That you are loved beyond your years.

A love so consuming,
A love so vast,
A love so immense
That not even the ventricles in your brain
Could possibly comprehend.

The Book I Never Read

I began my walk to work at 6:30 a.m.
The brisk summer air greeted my face.
I was ready for my nine-hour day.
Regardless of what my day off had brought,
I was ready.

Or so I thought.
But nothing could prepare me
For my first loss of a patient,
Especially when the patient was you
And you were more than a patient to me.

You were my buddy,
My friend,
My inspiration.
What we had was special.
What we had *is* special.

Because I spent months getting to know you
And greeting your family,
And I spent weeks getting beaten
In Uno, Scrabble Flash, and War;
And I spent days getting pranked
By your devious smile;
And I spent hours discussing baking
And the cakes you made for your sibling.

And I spent today
Grieving your loss.
My supervisor told me to let my heart lead the way
As wet tears grazed my face,

And my heart became angry
Because I loved you so much.
And so I bolted through the hospital doors
And looked to the sky.

You won't be my last,
But you were my first.
And today I set the path
Of losses to come,
And I choose to feel what's inside
And not shove it away.

I am so grateful
For the time you gave to me,
Because it has changed my life.
Thank you for showing me
That it's okay to be human
While still being a child life professional.

Today, I got in my car
And drove to my hometown,
Somewhere between badgers and trolls,
And I baked a dozen cupcakes
For a patient I adored
To celebrate their life.

Academy of Challenges

All it really takes
Is one step forward
In the right direction
To not only change your life
But also the lives of those around you.

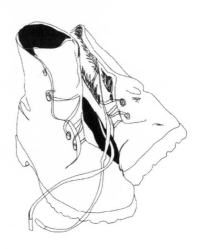

Real-Life Adults

Today, I am thankful
For roundtable meetings
With the child life team
And insightful conversation
That allows me to debrief.

With the odds of competition that were stacked
against me,
I could have interned anywhere in the country,
Or not at all.
But somehow I got fortunate,
And this hospital chose me.

And because of that fortune,
I have the opportunity
To learn, grow, and prosper
From so many strong and powerful women
Sitting with me at this table.

They share with me practices of self-love
And coping strategies to get through the days.
They listen to my struggles
Of bereavement and boundaries
And offer advice that's seasoned with wisdom.

I may not say it enough
At the roundtable meetings,
Because I am taking it all in
And storing it in my heart,

But thank you for impacting my life.

A Trying Oath

When I first looked at you,
I knew you had your daddy's eyes.
When his eyes met yours,
I knew how much he loved you
And how badly he wanted your pain to stop.

Your mother is beautiful
In the way she holds you tight.
She tells us you've been hurt before,
And I can see it in her face,
The fear that we may do the same.

It is not my promise to make,
Yet I want to say it anyway,
That we will not hurt you
In the ways the others did,
And we will do our best to help you.

In the procedure room,
You begin to cry and scream,
"Save me, Mommy!
"Save me, Daddy!"
And I hear you so loud and clear.

But in order to save you,
Sweet child,
We need to figure out what's wrong,
And that may take a little poking
And cause a little distraught.

    You may not understand now,
    And you may not understand later,
    That everything we are doing
    Is to keep you alive
    And to kill your cancer.

Faith in the Future

In class I learned
That it is called a crescent moon
When your red blood cells become misshapen.
And in class I learned
That sickle cell anemia has no cure.

But what you taught me today
Is something I never learned in school:
No matter how many pain crises you have,
You never give up
And you never give in.

Your voice was quiet,
But your eyes were fierce
As you told me your dream
To turn your condition into motivation,
To become a doctor to help others like you.

I Raced to Your Side

We received a page
That you needed something
To do with your hands
So we brought stress balls and fidgets,
But you didn't want any of that.

Perhaps all you wanted
Was the hand of your mother
Or sister or girlfriend.
Perhaps the only thing sensory you were craving
Was love.

Rainbow Posters & Native Songs

Rehabilitation does not come easy
For the adolescent involved
In an accident
That could have been fatal.

I cannot begin to imagine
The pain they must feel,
But I can see the bruises
And I can try to understand.

By establishing trust
And building rapport,
I learn what coping strategies
They have used in the past.

I bring in poster boards and paint
And let their creativity lead the way
As they play me songs
Important to their culture.

They are strong.
They are brave.
They are living.

Wake Up

I can tell you what it's like
To see a nurse
Collapse in tears
And break that robotic boundary
We all pretend we have.

I can tell you what it's like
To lose a patient
Who once had a bright and promising future,
And in a second
They were gone.

I can tell you what it's like
To watch a girlfriend pace the halls
Wiping tears from her eyes
Attempting to gain strength
To return to the PICU.

I can tell you what it's like
To be livid with childhood cancer
ALL, AML, neuroblastoma, osteosarcoma.
None of them receive enough funding,
And all of them take children's lives.

I can tell you what it's like,
Every day,
Every week,
Cancer kills another child,
And I can tell you what it's like . . .

But I don't want to,
Nor should I have to.
If we all came together,
Resources alike,
Maybe, just maybe, we could save one child's life.

You Remembered Me

I always loved Peter Pan
Because I wanted to stay young
Forever,
But today . . .
Today, I grew up.

As a child life intern,
I provide distraction
For children going through procedures
Such as port access and deaccess
And IV starts.

Today, I provided distraction
All on my own
And completely alone
For a young girl getting an IV placed
For the umpteenth time.

I entered the room
And began introducing myself
To a family I was familiar with.
But I am only an intern
And they meet dozens of people daily.

But the patient's mother
Stopped me in my tracks
As she told me, "I know who you are."
And I bit my lip
To hide my pride of remembrance.

I knew exactly how the girl coped
And I came prepared
With Mario Run on my iPad,
A stress ball in my hand,
And a calming voice to help her through.

She did so well,
And they were able to find a vein this time.
Her parents were grateful for me,
Yet I am thankful for them
For advocating for their child's needs.

Today, I grew up.
I provided distraction
All on my own
And completely alone.
Goodbye, Peter Pan.

Relax, 22-Year-Old, Relax

As I come home to write
This entry of mine,
I am lost
And unsure of what to say
Because we had six deaths last week.

I am feeling renewed and refreshed.
We did not have one today
And maybe we won't have one tomorrow.
So right now, I will be thankful
For this moment to breathe.

This moment to laugh,
This moment to smile,
This moment to take advantage of
And watch *The Bachelorette* with my friends
Because I am not grieving tonight.

At Least She Was Kind

We are not a zoo,
Nor are we art on display.
We are not for your entertainment,
Nor are we a show on Broadway.
We are a children's hospital.

We are not here for your camera crew
Or your social media.
We are not here to gawk at
Or to boost your ego.
We are a children's hospital.

I Want to Help You, But I Don't Know How

It has just stopped raining
And we are outside
At a special donations event.
There are so many cameras
And so many men in suits.

But all I am focused on
Is you
And how you are coping,
Because there are tears in your eyes.
This has to be so damn hard.

To listen to the story
Of a boy in remission
When your child is here
Living with cancer.
It has to be so damn hard.

Another Night, Another Cupcake

I haven't been sleeping well this week.
It could be the storms,
It could be the sirens,
It could be the helicopters,
It could be my restless mind.

Or it could be because
Every time my head hits the pillow,
I dream of you
And all I want to do
Is bring you back.

Back out of my mind
And onto the floor,
Or back into the kitchen
With your family
And back to me.

But that's not how dreams work.

Call Me Shaq's Girlfriend

Have you ever felt like Santa in June?
Because today I did
When I delivered the news
That Shaquille O'Neal was on his way
To spend time with our children and families.

He is as tall as they say
But also very kind.
He lit up the eyes
Of all patients and parents
As he walked the halls.

So many workers
Just wanted a glimpse
While I simply reminded them,
"This is not for you.
It is for the kids."

Celebrity visits can be so hectic
To plan and facilitate,
But it's so worth it
To see the boy living with cancer
Meet the man he's idolized

It is worth every second of frustration
To see the boy who politely says no
To games and crafts
Raise up his arm
To flex with Shaq.

Childhood Memories

On the day I was born,
My father gave me something special
Without having any idea
Just how impacting it would be
For the rest of my life.

He bought me a stuffed elephant
Dressed in baby pink and baby blue
With cotton balls as buttons,
And this elephant has been with me
Everywhere.

I met a brave little girl today
Who has the same name
As the elephant that I hold dear,
And I treated her
As I always treated him.

With kindness,
With respect,
With protection,
And a little bit of silliness
As she got her IV placed.

And we talked about the Fontan,
A certain kind of surgical procedure
Done on the heart
Of a child
With one single functional ventricle.

How brave is she
To go through something
Most of us will never go through
In a lifetime.
She is so brave.

And her mother and father are lovely.
Her mother is so nurturing
And clearly understands little minds,
And her father is supportive
In the way he meets her eyes.

This child brought me back to my childhood,
But I was never as brave as her
As I fought pretend battles
With my stuffed elephant
With the same name as this little girl.

Natural Disasters

Before interning at this hospital,
I spent over 160 hours
As their volunteer,
But in those four years,
I had never seen what I saw today.

I have volunteered during rain,
I have volunteered during snow,
I have volunteered during intense heat,
But never have I ever volunteered during
A tornado warning.

At approximately 4:15 today,
A voice on the loudspeaker announced
That a tornado warning was in full spring
So we sprung into action
To protect our kids.

All children and families
Were brought into the hallways,
Beds and all.
The doors were shut
And the blinds were closed.

For over 30 minutes,
Families sat in the halls
And our staff ensured
That every fear was conquered,
And that every child was safe.

The majority of our children were calm,
And I suppose I have a theory
As to how that could be:
Perhaps the threat of a tornado
Is nothing to the child fighting cancer.

A History of Empathy

When I was nine years old,
I began my journey with chronic pain.
For thirteen years,
I haven't gone a day
Without anguish in my body.

The pain is nearly everywhere.

> My legs,
>   My knees,
>   My back,
>   My neck,
>   My shoulders,
>   My mouth,
>   My stomach,
>   My eyes.

It has been a high-pain week,
And I am exhausted.
I worked nine hours today
And then spent three hours
In Urgent Care.

Being poked and prodded,
Receiving fluids for pain management
To get me through the week.
I work again tomorrow
And am seeing more doctors the day after that.

My chronic pain is invisible
The majority of the time,
But that doesn't mean it's not real;
Because I promise that it is,
And that reality drives me

To always trust my kids
When they say they hurt,
But it doesn't show up on the scans
Because I've been there a million times
And I'll go through it a million more

To let a child know
That I believe them.

Beautiful Days

I lived in my memories today
Watching our story unfold
On the screen inside my mind,
Reliving every memory
And every smile you brought to me.

Every toy you threw in my direction,
Every time you held your microphone tight,
Every time I was able to read to you,
Even the time you rode a toy car down the halls.
I am seeing it all.

I have known you for a few months now
And I have talked to your caregivers often
About how they are doing
And how I can help,
But I'm afraid I just can't help right now.

Or maybe I can,
Maybe I did
When I helped create ink prints
Of your little hands
And little feet.

When I rubbed your hand
So softly
So gently
And tickled your fingers
With the feeling of plaster.

When I talked to your sibling
To assess their needs
And when I listened to your heartbeat song
Our music therapist created
For your family to keep.

I would like to think
That I provided some healing
In the memory-making
And if you believed in reincarnation,
I'll see you next time, little one.

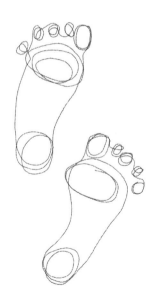

Rooting for You

I am in awe of you.
You have every reason
To be unpleasant,
Yet here you are
Greeting me with kindness.

You watch your daughter
Walk the halls,
And I cannot begin to imagine
Where your family has been
In these last six months.

But you are here now.
She is here now
And every second
You are waiting
For your phone to ring.

She's on the transplant list
To receive a lung.
All of your work is done.
You are so strong, Mama.
I am in awe of you.

You Are a Wonderful Mom

It is a lot of pressure
When a family has never
Met child life,
And it is up to me
To make a good impression.

You tell me your baby
Has had a lot of poking
And a lot of prodding
Done in his life
Because he was a preemie.

And you tell me that you hover,
But that makes perfect sense to me
When you have a child
Such as yours
That you love so dearly.

When the vascular access team comes in,
I advocate for comfort positioning,
But unfortunately that cannot be done
And he must leave the home of your arms
To go to his crib.

As they struggle to find a vein,
I redirect his attention
To my red tambourine
And I sing nursery rhymes
To keep him calm.

We've tried two hands and a foot
And still no IV.
I know they're trying,
But I know you're hurting
So I tell you it won't be long.

When the IV is placed,
I give you a musical toy set
Donated from our community
For you to use
When we cannot be there.

You look at me with such intensity in your eyes
And gratitude in your smile,
As I say goodbye to your son,
I think to myself,
I think I've left a good impression.

Here I Am

Today was the first day
I carried the unit pager,
And for the first time,
I didn't feel that I could do this
But that I already was all along.

And that feeling
Brought such joy to my heart.
I am growing so much.
I am becoming independent.
I am independent.

Let Love In

Oh, my dear,
I hear your screams
From outside your room
As you say that no one loves you
And that you're all alone in this fight.

My heart breaks a little,
Because I know it's not true,
But if you believe any of that,
We need to do a better job
Of getting you to let us in.

I watch the nurses grow tired
As they try their best to soothe you,
And you continue to yell,
But it makes sense,
Doesn't it?

A young girl
Living with cancer
And upset with the world.
It makes sense,
It makes sense to me.

The Best Days

Every day has impacted me
For the betterment of my mind,
But today has impacted me
In ways I'm struggling
To put into words.

Because I met a family today
That showed me
The true definition of love.
My heart is happy.
I am so happy.

When I first met you,
I commented on the beautiful
Color of your eyes,
And your father told me
That you are nonverbal.

A child with hydrocephalus
And craniofacial anomalies:
You are here
To have a procedure
On your brain.

But that doesn't matter to me,
Because if you can understand me,
I want to be heard.
You deserve as much attention
As the verbal child next door.

You begin to play catch with me
And your father in the hallway.
Even though that's not allowed,
I let it slide
Because you're having fun.

When your father appears to grow tired,
I kindly offer him a break,
But he looks at me and says,
"I love my children.
I love my family."

And I can't help but think to myself,
How lucky would I be one day
To have a child such as yours
And a man that loves us wholeheartedly?
I would be so lucky.

Thank You for the Invitation

Have you ever had a two-poem day?
Before writing these poems,
I was struggling
With which patient to choose
And what story to tell.

But then I decided,
Why not simply write both?
Because they both deserve
To be heard
And so here I am.

A teenage patient who is always polite
But turns me down day after day,
But not today
Because today,
She invited me to play.

So there I sat
Among nurses and her family.
We played one round
Of Imploding Kittens,
And I was eliminated first.

But I didn't care
Because she was having fun,
And then we played Boggle,
A race against the clock
To connect every letter.

As we shared our words,
Her caregiver said
That she and I were like twins
In the way our brains functioned
To create words from the tiles.

And I thought to myself
How grateful I was
To be compared to her.
She is witty, kind, and brave.
She is.

Hold Her Dearly, Young Man

When a child has cancer,
It seems like they meet
Dozens of people a day,
Faces both old and new,
All with a different job to do.

And so I've never set
My expectations high
Of a patient or family
Remembering who I am
Because I am one of the many.

There is a boy with cancer
I've gotten to know
With a caring and loving
Grandmother in his life
Who is here every day.

This boy and I
Have had numerous play adventures
And endearing conversations;
He wishes to be a doctor
At this hospital one day.

I was in his room this morning
To check on his fever
And assess his needs.
He was feeling so ill,
But he still managed to smile.

And as I turned to the door,
His grandmother said,
"Thank you for checking in on us
Every single day
To make sure we have what we need."

It's his last week of chemotherapy.
And then he is done,
In remission, as they say,
And as much as I love the two of them,
I hope that they never return.

Silly Expectations

I cried last night.
It lasted for a while.
I began to miss
What I've lost
Or *who* I've lost.

I woke up this morning
Feeling so drained
And found myself wondering why.
Oh, sweet child,
What a silly question.

I'm working over
Forty hours a week unpaid
And I'm completing
Two courses of homework online
While maintaining a social life.

All of this learning
And all of this living
Is so draining
Physically, mentally, emotionally.
I'm merely trying to stay afloat.

All of the Birds He Has Yet to Make

I'm thinking of all
The beautiful children
I will miss
When I switch rotations
And can no longer see my kids.

There's something about timing
And the way things seem to work out.
As I prepared myself to say goodbye
To a young boy with leukemia,
I realized that he, too, was leaving.

Another cycle of chemotherapy completed,
Which made my departure
Much more organic
And easier for myself to bear
Because I wasn't leaving him.

For he was leaving us
And I knew he would have fun at home
With his two older siblings
And endearing parents.
I knew he would be okay.

No Guidebook

It is my last day in this rotation.
How am I supposed to move on
To another population
Or another supervisor
When my heart is this content?

How am I supposed to move on
From the boy I just met
Who is fighting Hodgkin's lymphoma?
How am I supposed to move on
From his beautiful welcoming family?

How am I supposed to move on
From patients and families knowing my name
And staff collaborating with me
For the care of a child?
How am I supposed to move on

When I don't want to,
Because my heart is here
My calling is here,
With these children and these families.
Tell me how I'm supposed to let go.

You Did Well, Love

I sat at the roundtable
With three of my supervisors
And a ten-page packet
Sitting in front of me.
Time for evaluation.

My professor prepared me
For this day
By telling me to expect ones and twos
Because I am just starting
And I am always learning.

This makes sense to me.
I would never pretend that
I'm something I'm not,
And this was my first rotation.
I am still a student.

So you could probably imagine
The joy in my heart
As I received fours and fives
And my supervisor told me
Interns aren't typically rated this high.

And high is what I feel,
As high as a kite
Or bird in the sky.
I am so high,
And no one can bring me down.

Expansion

One of my favorite things
Is seeing child life specialists
Honing in their craft
And expanding their skill set
To an alternative setting.

Child life specialists are not only in hospitals.
They are utilized in various locations:
Advocacy centers, funeral homes, dental offices,
Hospice organizations, sports medicine clinics.
They could be beneficial anywhere.

Anywhere there is a child.

Busy Minds in High-Traffic Times

After the horrid week we've had
With almost losing our dog,
My mother and I hopped in the Jeep
And drove to Chicago
For another child life site visit.

The advocacy center is a beautiful building
With brightly colored walls
And an outdoor play space.
It's hard to imagine
That this isn't a daycare.

It's where children come
To give their statements
Of being abused.
It's where children come
When someone's hurt them.

In a dreadfully intimate way
That no individual should ever go through,
Yet children do.
Every single day,
A child walks through these doors.

But child life helps make it better
With play and support.
The team tries to help every child
Feel like a child
Because that's what they deserve.

The Importance of Girls Being Kind to Girls

I spent numerous hours
Independently planning and orchestrating
An activity group
For seven beautiful girls
With sickle cell disease.

As I sat in my car, I unfolded the notes
Of encouragement and kindness
That I had each of us create
And I began to tear up
With each kind sentiment a child had written.

Although our time was brief,
The messages will last a lifetime,
The moments shared will be remembered,
And the meaning will stay
With us always.

Sibling Similarities

It was my first day
Of my second rotation
In outpatient clinics,
And I am grateful to experience
A variety of procedures.

One procedure I witnessed today
Was the removal of a cast and pins
From a young boy's arm.
He appeared to be nervous;
His parents were calm and collected.

But what stuck out to me most
Was the reaction
Of his younger sister
As she cried, "I'm scared,"
And sat in her father's lap.

It was like I was looking at myself
From eighteen years ago
And how I would have reacted
Had I been in the same situation
As that child.

Protective of my older brother,
Wanting to keep my hero
Free from pain
As he had always strived to do the same
For me.

Soccer Player

When I was inpatient,
I met a young girl and her family
Whom I treasured dearly
Because they were so kind
And so loving.

It had been over a month
Since I had last heard
How she was doing,
But today I was told
That she comes in weekly for labs.

When I entered her room,
Her whole family exploded in excitement
As they yelled my name
And recognized my presence.
It felt so good to be known.

They were as delightful
As the first day I met them.
I was sad to leave my first rotation,
Yet I am so happy
To have this family back.

I'm Sorry

My heart is hurting.
My mind is worrying.
One of my patients
Was rushed
To emergency surgery.

From My Television Screen to Right in Front of Me

I was so excited
And a little nervous
As I walked to work
Envisioning my first day
In the emergency department.

The environment is so different
And fast-paced
Compared to every other area
I've worked in before,
And I absolutely love it.

I love the adrenaline
That runs through my body
When a trauma is paged
And I know that I can be there
To make a difference for a child and family.

Two traumas today.
A young child attacked
By a dog
And another young child
Struck by a car.

I was able to provide support
For both children
And both of their families.
And I felt called to be there
By something bigger than myself.

Celebrity Crush

You looked at me
With bright eyes
And asked me if I knew Harry Styles.
When I said yes,
Your eyes became brighter.

You told me you loved him
As you endured your chemotherapy
For rhabdomyosarcoma
And that your bedroom walls
Were filled with posters of Harry.

And I wish I had the power
To grant wishes
And bring him here
To serenade you,
But I am not a genie.

Please Know . . .

I am in bed
Wishing so badly
That I could reach out
To the individual
Who came to clinic today.

The one I went to high school with.

But that would break boundaries,
So here I am
Hoping they are okay,
But also hoping they know I'm here
Even if I'm not right now.

She Radiates

If you want to know what true beauty
Looks like,
Look at the seven-year-old girl
With astrocytoma
Who shaved her head today.

Never Leave Yourself Behind

I am not sure how I am feeling
About my internship ending
Next month,
But I do know that this uncertainty
Is frightening.

I have grown so much
Since I began,
Yet I am still
The lost 22-year-old
I was in May.

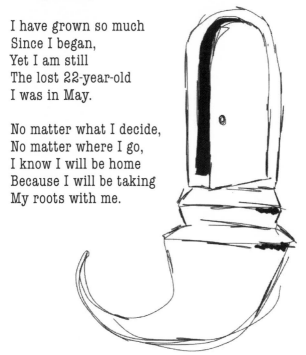

No matter what I decide,
No matter where I go,
I know I will be home
Because I will be taking
My roots with me.

Hoverboards

A charming young boy arrived in our ER tonight,
An arm fracture caused by a fall,
And he would need to be sedated
So the medical team could put it back in place.
He was so nervous as he played with his hands.

So we talked for quite a while,
And I answered all of his questions
And spent time doing damage control
When an employee used language
He couldn't understand.

I felt needed.
I felt valued.
I felt confident
That he would do just fine
Because he understood.

Help Me

Detachment has never been a strength of mine,
But I have to let go
Of the two PICU families I no longer serve
Even though their journeys aren't yet over.
I have to let go . . .

Progress

I distracted alone in clinic
For the first time.
I felt independent again.
A child needed his port accessed,
A child I had met before.

I respected his coping plan,
Because what's the use of creating one
If you never use it?
So we played and we counted
And he smiled through it all.

Fix Me

Today was a terrible day
For my chronic pain.
My knees kept popping
And snapping
And clicking.

How am I supposed to wait two weeks
Until my next appointment?
How am I supposed to cope
When I can barely walk?
Because every step is filled with pain.

I am so excited for September.
I hope they can operate.
I hope this will all be over,
Or I will be doing nerve blocks
For the rest of my life.

We Are All Overwhelmed

My internship has changed.
I am no longer in clinics.
I am no longer in the emergency department.
I no longer work the days I once did.
Everything has changed.

And I am really struggling right now,
But my team needs me,
Or *the* team needs me.
Because they're not really mine.
This is all just temporary.

Bubble Bath, Please

I slept past my alarm this morning.
I am worn out in all capacities.
I am merely trying to adjust
To my new schedule
And this new environment.

I am in surgery now
With a wonderful child life specialist,
But I mentally and physically struggled
To simply keep up,
Because a lot is being asked of me.

And I think that is fair to say
When everything changes
And you must step up,
I think it is fair to recognize
That this is a lot for an intern to handle.

I worked ten hours today,
And I work at 6:30 a.m. again tomorrow.
I wasn't supposed to work, but now I do
And I am desperately craving a day off
And I think that is fair to say.

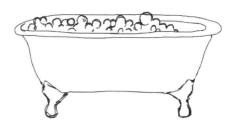

Buried in an Avalanche

I am not ready.
I am overwhelmed.
How am I supposed to be independent
When I began only yesterday?
It's okay that I'm not okay right now.

I Stayed, I Promise

Whenever I read her name,
My heart hurts a little.
But my soul becomes happy,
Because any child with her name
Reminds me of her spirit.

You certainly lived up to her name
While creating your own.
Your kind and gentle soul
Seemed uncanny
In your teenage body.

We were talking in-depth
About your dream career
And your knowledge in music
When your eyes began rolling
And my hands found the call light.

I had never seen a seizure
Until I was watching yours.
The nurses came running in
And I moved to the side,
Telling you, "We're right here."

When your nurse dismissed me
From your room,
I asked her to let you know
That I didn't just leave you
And that I stayed as long as I could.

Sweet Boy

My favorite memories of high school
Are managing the boys' soccer team
With my brother and best friend,
And ever since those days,
I've bonded so easily with adolescent boys.

My heart is not frozen
When it comes to this career.
Certain situations trigger certain emotions.
My heart beats harder
When working with adolescent boys.

Boys who were raised to be polite and kind.
Boys with beautiful parents.
My heart ached a little today
When parents said goodbye to their son
Who was having brain surgery.

My heartstrings tugged and pulled
As I imagined what it would be like
If this happened to a teammate of mine.
And my heart felt for this boy and his family
And it felt hard.

A Day of Days

The first tears that fell
Were out of frustration.
I felt like I had to justify
My exhaustion and stress.
I felt so utterly misunderstood.

The last tears that fell
Were out of validation.
A personalized cookie and note
Left on my desk
From a patient who finished radiation.

Passed out on the Floor Sober

My best friend's birthday is today.
I was upbeat at dinner,
But then we went back to the apartment
And my exhaustion won the fight
As I sat hunched on the floor with a blanket
Unable to move a muscle.

I was supposed to go out tonight
To celebrate, dance, and be youthful;
But instead, I collapsed on the floor
And took a cab home
And cried myself to sleep.
I just want to be 22 again.

Pretty Rad

Her hair was colored in a rainbow array.
Her smile was so genuine
As she told me she didn't know
How she reacted to needles,
Because this was her first time.

Her first surgery.
Her first IV.
Her first time having her hair
Colored so brightly.

And she triumphed through them all
As we engaged in conversation
About returning to school and summer vacation.
During induction, we watched music videos
As medleys by the Beatles sang her to sleep.

You Did Nothing Wrong

I've enjoyed the challenge
That surgery brings
Because I am so comfortable
In the inpatient world
And this is all so new to me.

But it wasn't so new today
When a ten-month-old was added
To our status board.
It wasn't so new today
When I needed to comfort a father.

A father who's had an unbearable 24 hours.
A father who was told his ten-month-old
Might have cancer.
And so I did the best I could to support him.
I listened.

I listened to his fears.
I listened to his frustrations with staff and work.
I listened to his self-blame.
I listened to his heart beat.
And I heard his love.

Atlantis

I was late yesterday.
My town is underwater.
I was late today.
I had a doctor's appointment.
I am late now
In writing this fragment.

I cannot stop the flood.
I cannot control the test results.
I cannot get my mind to quiet.
I feel helpless.
I may as well be drowning in the waters.

Listen with Your Eyes

Why do some people assume
That nonverbal children
Cannot understand or hear you?
I am not an expert in medicine,
But I would like to think
I am an expert in communication.

And I know your precious child
Is communicating with me
When I smile widely at her
And she smiles back at me.
Every single smile is returned.
This has to be more than a coincidence.

You Don't Have to Be Strong

Oh, sweet mother,
I hear your cries
And I see your worry,
As it is clearly written
All over your face.

Your day should have been filled
With back-to-school shopping,
But instead you are here
In the surgical unit
Praying the surgeon can fix your son's arm.

I understand that it was emergent
And nothing you had planned for.
It's understandable that you're not calm
And that you're not collected
Because he's your beautiful boy.

I want to sit with you for hours
And calm your nerves,
But I have other children to see
And other mothers to soothe.
So, I leave you with this . . .

Familiar Faces

The year 2016 was monumental
For children with spinal muscular atrophy.
The first drug was approved for treatment.
I first learned about this medication in class
And then from a dear high school friend.

This sweet friend arrived in my unit today.
Another treatment in the books
To improve their strength.
I stopped by their room to say hello
And was greeted with warm hugs and smiles.

I commended them for their strides in school
And was impressed by their recent employment.
We took a photo together on their phone to capture
    the memory
Of two friends meeting together in the hospital by
    chance.
This is why I am grateful to have grown up in a
    small town.

You Know Your Child Best

A photo board hangs on the wall.
At first, I don't even see it
And I kick myself for that later.
How can I not see
A boy who is filled with so much personality?

A mother who must have spent hours
Creating a resource
That introduces her nonverbal son
To every member of the multidisciplinary team
At each healthcare appointment.

What a wonderful way to communicate,
To let us inside his life.
His life of school, dogs, and *The Goonies*.
His life outside of the hospital walls.
There is a person inside that body.

And with the rush of the surgery flow,
Perhaps it is easy to forget or move along
With the hustle and bustle of procedures;
But there is a boy who deserves
To be known.

My Younger Self

I wish I could tell you
That I've been here before
So many times.
And I wish I could tell you
That I truly understand.

Some individuals you connect with more than others,
And tonight I connected with you and your mother
Because I've been in this emergency department
So many times
As a patient and not just as a worker.

I, too, had an enema in this ER
Done by a physician I now work with.
I, too, know how uncomfortable this can be
And how frustrating it is not to receive answers
When you've been searching your whole life.

What I couldn't tell you tonight
I want to write to you now.
Your body does not hate you;
It just does not understand
How to love you right now.

So treat yourself with respect
And be your own advocate,
And doctors will shake their heads
Time and time again.
And it will hurt.

It will hurt so badly,
So turn to your mother for support
And let the anger fuel you
To continue fighting for your health
Because you deserve to be at peace with yourself.

Please Make It

There is no time for supervisors
To hold your hand
When level-one traumas arrive,
So get out of the way
And help however you can.

I am so proud of myself
For stepping up tonight
And taking the young sibling
Of a teenager hit by a truck
Into the playroom.

I am not sure if he quite understood
The severity of the scenario at hand
As he giggled and played cars with me
In a strange new environment
Without his caregivers by his side.

He was so well-mannered and polite.
I don't know if I have ever met a boy his age
Who was that kind,
Especially when I was a stranger
And staff were running frantic.

He must have an excellent older sibling
As a role model to have learned from,
And I hope he can continue learning.
I hope his sibling will be okay.
All I can do is hope.

All That She Is, All That I Strive to Be

Two twelve-hour shifts
In a row
On a holiday weekend,
And I am feeling so comfortable
And so content.

But I wouldn't have been able to do it
Physically, mentally, or emotionally
Without my supervisor.
She is one of the most genuine beings
I have ever been blessed to meet.

I hope she knows how much she is valued,
How much she *should* be valued.
Because I have seen how she can positively impact
The experience of a patient and family.
I hope she knows that.

It's Been Interesting

It was my last day in surgery.
I am currently uncertain
If I am happy or sad about it ending.
Perhaps a bit of both.

I wasn't interested in working in surgery
When I was first told about my new rotation.
I think I enjoyed it more than I thought.
I was challenged in ways I hadn't been before.

But I also felt like I was constantly failing,
And I am not sure which is better:
To be comfortable and succeeding
Or to be learning and struggling.

Onward I Go

My child life internship is officially over
After three and a half months of dedication
And over 600 hours of hard work.
My time at this hospital
Has come to an end.

After six semesters as a child life volunteer,
After twelve internship applications,
After seven internship interviews,
After five internship offers,
This chapter is closed.

It is so bittersweet
Because I will miss
This child life department so much.
And I will miss the patients and families
I had to leave today.

But at the same time,
I am ready.
I am ready for an emotional and mental cleanse.
I am ready to focus on what is next for me.
I am ready to begin again.

About the Author

Taran Lancaster is a 22-year-old currently flourishing in an idyllic small town in Wisconsin. She recently obtained certification as a child life specialist and is searching for her next adventure in her field of work. Taran is extremely passionate about advocacy for mental health, recognizing chronic illnesses, fitness, and creating truthful and inspiring social media content. In her free time, she enjoys petting all of the dogs, shopping, watching movies, photography, immersing herself in bubble baths, and traveling.

Connect with the Author

Instagram.com/chronicallytaran

Leave a Review

If you enjoyed *The Fragments of a Child Life Intern*, please stop by Amazon or Goodreads to leave me a review. Thanks to reviews, indie authors can reach more readers just like you.

Made in the
USA
Middletown, DE